SPOOKY HALLOWEEN PUZZLES

• by Sonia Black •

Illustrations by Patrick Merrell

SCHOLASTIC INC.

New York Toronto London Auckland Sydney
Mexico City New Delhi Hong Kong Buenos Aires

ISBN 0-439-68017-4

12 11 10 9 8 7 6 5 4 3 2 1   4 5 6 7 8 9/0

Printed in the U.S.A.   40

First printing, October 2004

MYSTERY MESSAGE

The vowels are missing! The vowels are missing! Fill in A, E, I, O, or U in the correct spaces and you will see a special Halloween message.

W_LC_M_ ,   TR_CK-_R-TR_ _T_RS.

C_M_   _N_ ,   C_M_   _LL.

C_M_   _ _ T, C_M_   _ _ T

WH_R_V_R   Y_ _   _R_.

C_M_   H_V_   B_G   F_N

_T   TH_   H_PPY

H_LL_W_ _ N   M_NST_R

B_SH!

GHOSTS EVERYWHERE!

What's Halloween without a few ghosts? There are eighteen of them hiding in this word find. Look up, down, backward, forward, and diagonally. Circle each one you see.

```
T T G H O S T S O H G S
T S O H G H O S T H H G
G O O G O T T T O G O H
S H G H O S T S H H S O
T G O O G O T O S O T S
G H O S T H G H O S T T
H G O T T G H G S T G S
```

FUNNY FACES

Happy? Sad? Mad? Glad? Draw a line from each pumpkin face to the correct label.

HAPPY

SAD

ANGRY

SLEEPY

SURPRISED

SILLY

WHAT YOU SEE IS WHAT YOU GET

What a spooky scene! Take a good look all around. Pay close attention to everything you see. Then turn the page for a quick memory test.

TESTING, TESTING!

How many of these questions can you answer *without* looking back at the spooky scene?

1. There's a full moon. True or False? _____

2. How many crows are in the tree? _____

3. How many owls are in the tree? _____

4. What is hanging from the tree? _____

5. What flies above the house? _____

6. Name the three things that are in the windows. _____

_____

7. What message is written on the road sign?

_____

_____

8. Who is walking by the house? _____

9. How is he dressed? _____

10. What flies over his head? _____

FRIGHT NIGHT

On this dark and spooky night, two scared kids are lost in the cemetery. Help them find their way out—fast! And keep them away from the ghosts!

HIDE-AND-SEEK

Each sentence below contains a hidden, Halloween-related word. Underline the word or words when you see them. The first one is done for you.

1. Amy loves playing <u>host</u> at her parents' parties.

2. With his quick wit, Charles would make a great comedian.

3. "What's up, Ump?" Kingsley cheerfully greeted Mr. Townsend, the umpire of his baseball team.

4. Grace met E. R. Young at his law office to discuss her case.

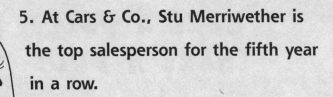

5. At Cars & Co., Stu Merriwether is the top salesperson for the fifth year in a row.

6. Peter and Bob lack Cathy's skill at public speaking.

7. Pat, Rick, and Johnny formed a singing group called Punks.

8. Because I had a lisp, I'd...er...sometimes be self-conscious when I...er...spoke.

9. The chef set the slices of ham on sterling silver trays.

10. Cedric, Andy, Cornelius, and Simon are on the high school baseball team.

HERE A BOO, THERE A BOO!

All the words in this puzzle have the letters B-O-O in them. Use the clues to help you fill in the missing letters.

1.	boo _	Something you read
2.	b _ oo _	A small stream
3.	boo _ _ _ _ _	A toy that comes back to you
4.	boo _	A loud sound
5.	b _ oo _	Something you sweep with
6.	b _ _ _ oo _	Something you inflate
7.	b _ oo _	What flowers do in spring
8.	b _ oo _	What flows through your veins
9.	boo _ _	Something to wear on your feet
10.	b _ _ _ _ oo _	A place to dance
11.	b _ _ _ _ _ _ oo _	Not the bride
12.	b _ _ _ oo _	A woodwind instrument

DOT'S ALL, FOLKS!

Connect the dots from A to Z and—
Abracadabra!—a Halloween fright sight
will appear.

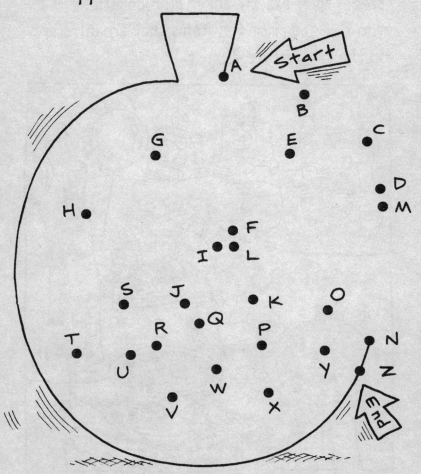

WHAT'S THE DIFFERENCE?

At first glance, these two Halloween party scenes look exactly alike. But look closer. Can you find and circle ten items that are different in the two pictures?

WORD UP!

Put on your thinking cap. How many new words can you find in the word GRAVEYARD? Write a word inside each tombstone.

R. I. P.

SEEING DOUBLE

Get ready to go batty! Two of these bats are exactly alike. Can you tell which ones they are?

ODD ONE OUT

One scarecrow is different from the rest. Can you find it?

MOVIE SCRAMBLE

Let's go to the movies! Fill in the answers to the clues in the blank spaces. Then unscramble the circled letters to find the name of an out-of-sight fright flick.

1. Knife, fork, ____

   Ⓞ — — — —

2. Our closest star

   Ⓞ — —

3. Silver and ____

   — Ⓞ — —

4. Opposite of leave

   — Ⓞ — —

5. Another word for bunny

   — — — — —Ⓞ

6. **Third month of the year**

 _ _ ◯ _ _

7. **Synonym for big**

 _ _ _ ◯ _

8. **Opposite of good-bye**

 ◯ _ _ _ _

9. **A holiday in spring**

 _ _ _ _ ◯ _

10. **Opposite of sell**

 _ ◯ _

11. **First meal of the day**

 ◯ _ _ _ _ _ _ _ _

12. **To run after**

 _ _ _ ◯ _

 ⬭ _ _ _ _ _ _ _ _ _ _ _ _ ⬭

COSTUME CROSSWORD

All kinds of costumed characters pop up at Halloween time. Use the clues to fill in the names of those that appear in this puzzle. The letters in the shaded boxes will spell out the name of one of the most famous tricksters of all time.

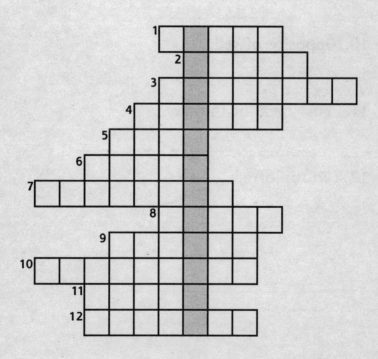

costumes

famous

1. Casper is one

2. A heavenly winged figure

3. The daughter of a king

4. A robber on the high seas

5. An infant

6. She casts spells

tricksters

7. A bony figure

8. This person assists the doctor

9. This creature has eight legs

10. A kind of dancer

11. A circus performer

12. Count Dracula is one

crossword

HAUNTED HOUSE MAZE

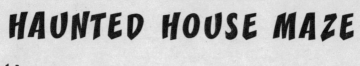

Yikes! A trick-or-treater is trapped in this haunted house. Help him find his way to the front door.

Start →

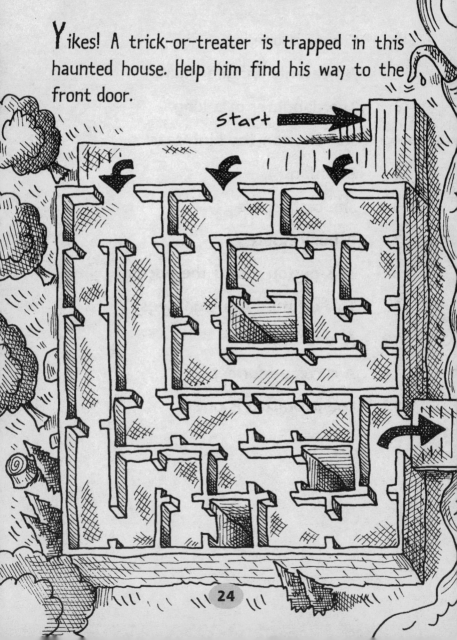

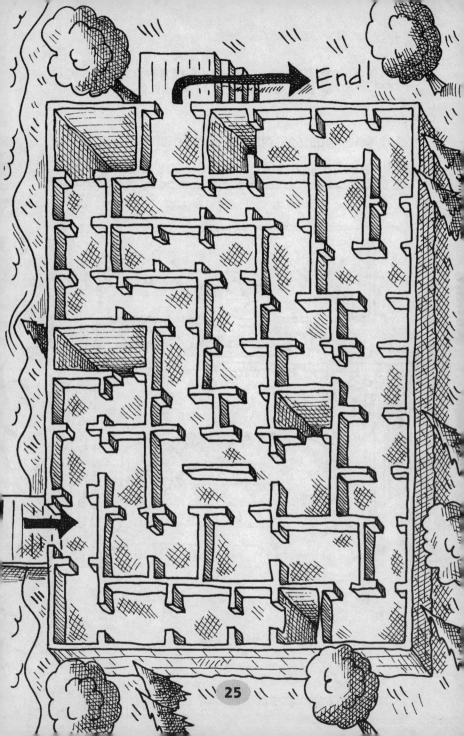

End!

SPIDER HUNT

Get out your spy glasses! There are ten spiders hiding in this picture. Can you spy them all?

CANDY-COATED CROSSWORD

Trick-or-treaters collect bags full of candy. Complete this do-it-yourself crossword puzzle with all the candy below. Some letters have been filled in to get you started.

Toffee   Chocolate
Caramel   Jelly beans
Licorice   Gummy worms
Lollipop   Tootsie Roll
Candy corn   Peppermint

SECRET MESSAGE

Use the clues to help you fill in the blanks. Then, write the letters in the matching numbered spaces in the puzzle boxes. When you're done, a ghostly message will appear.

1. It's not "yes"

$\overline{}\ \overline{}$
20 5

2. Cut the lawn

$\overline{}\ \overline{}\ \overline{}$
10 16 14

3. What you do with a needle and thread

$\overline{}\ \overline{}\ \overline{}$
7 11 3

4. Two thousand pounds

$\overline{}\ \overline{}\ \overline{}$
21 13 1

5. You see with this

$\overline{}\ \overline{}\ \overline{}$
9 15 8

6. Shake your head

$$\overline{12} \ \overline{2} \ \overline{18}$$

7. Popular toy, the yo- __

$$\overline{4} \ \overline{19}$$

8. Abbreviation for Unknown Universe

$$\overline{6} \ \overline{17}$$

1	2	3		4	5	6		7	8	9		10	11
	12	13	14		15	16	17		18	19	20	21	

GOING IN CIRCLES

The names of a special group of Halloween favorites are scrambled on page 33. To find out who they are, first complete the puzzle below.

Begin at START with the letter T. Move clockwise around the circle, and write every second letter after the T on the lines provided. When you have written all the letters, you will see a clue to help unscramble the scrambled names on page 33.

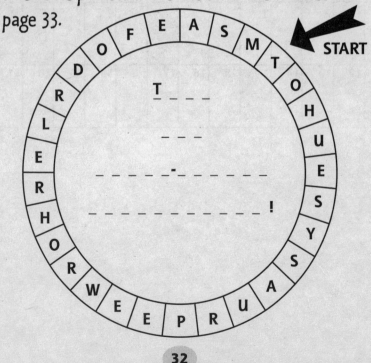

START

T _ _ _

_ _ _

_ _ _ _ _ _ - _ _ _ _

_ _ _ _ _ _ _ _ _ _ _ !

THE NAME GAME

1. **HET IIRDENELCB KUHL**

   _ _ _   _ _ _ _ _ _ _ _ _ _

   _ _ _ _

2. **MTNBAA**

   _ _ _ _ _ _

3. **ONWRDE AOMWN**

   _ _ _ _ _ _   _ _ _ _ _

4. **DRMPISENA**

   _ _ _ _ _ _ _-_ _ _

5. **PRANSMUE**

   _ _ _ _ _ _ _ _

ORDER! ORDER!

*E*EEEEEEK! These pictures are out of order. Number them correctly so that they tell a story from start to finish. Use the boxes in the upper left-hand corner of each picture.

HALLOWEEN HA-HA'S

The answers to these hilarious Halloween jokes are sure to tickle your funny bone. But they are written in code. Use the chart below to crack the code for a hearty laugh and a half.

Alphabet Code:

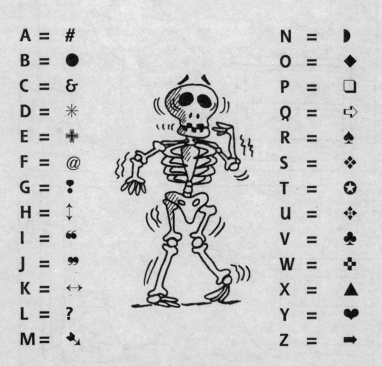

A = #	N = ◗
B = ●	O = ◆
C = &	P = ❑
D = ✳	Q = ⇨
E = ✚	R = ♠
F = @	S = ❖
G = ❢	T = ✪
H = ↕	U = ✛
I = "	V = ♣
J = "	W = ✦
K = ↔	X = ▲
L = ?	Y = ♥
M = ⬎	Z = ➡

1. Why didn't the skeleton cross the road?

↕ ✚ ↕ # ✳ ◗ ◆ ❢✥ ✪ ❖

_ _ _ _ _ _ _ _ _ _ _.

2. What did the mother vampire do when her son had a cold?

❖ ↕ ✚ ❢ # ♣ ✚ ↕ ❝ ➴

_ _ _ _ _ _ _ _ _ _ _

& ◆ @ @ ❝ ◗ ➴ ✚ ✳ ❝ & ❝ ◗ ✚

_ _ _ _ _ _ _ _ _ _ _ _ _ _ _.

3. What did the boy monster say to the girl monster on their blind date?

✳ ◆ ❤ ◆ ✥ ● ✚ ? ❝ ✚ ♣ ✚ ❝ ◗

_ _ _ _ _ _ _ _ _ _ _ _ _ _

? ◆ ♣ ✚ # ✪ @ ❝ ♠ ❖ ✪ @ ♠ ❝ ❢ ↕ ✪

_ _ _ _ _ _ _ _ _ _ _ _ _ _ _ _ _?

CREATURE FEATURE

Beware! Monsters and frightening creatures are lurking in this word find. They are hidden down, backward, and forward. Find and circle them all. Then fill in the blank spaces with the leftover letters in the order they appear and you will see what all the creatures have in common.

Bigfoot
The Blob
Count Dracula
The Fly
Frankenstein
Godzilla
King Kong
The Mummy
The Swamp Thing
The Werewolf
The Wolfman
The Zombie

T	H	E	B	L	O	B	G	N	O	K	G	N	I	K	T	H
H	E	S	T	H	E	W	E	R	E	W	O	L	F	E	C	H
E	A	R	A	C	A	L	U	C	A	R	D	T	N	U	O	C
M	T	E	Y	L	F	E	H	T	H	E	Z	O	M	B	I	E
U	T	H	E	S	W	A	M	P	T	H	I	N	G	R	S	A
M	N	A	M	F	L	O	W	E	H	T	L	R	E	M	A	J
M	O	R	B	I	G	F	O	O	T	M	L	O	V	I	E	S
Y	T	N	I	E	T	S	N	E	K	N	A	R	F	A	R	S

_ _ _ _ _

_ _ _ _ _ _ _ _ _

_ _ _   _ _ _ _ _

_ _ _ _ _   _ _ _ _ _ !

39

MIXED-UP MESS

Uh-oh! The mummies are unraveling. Follow the tangled strips of cloth to discover which candy sack belongs to which mummy.

Puzzle Answers

Page 3
MYSTERY MESSAGE:
WELCOME, TRICK-OR-TREATERS. COME ONE, COME ALL.
COME OUT, COME OUT WHEREVER YOU ARE. COME
HAVE BIG FUN AT THE HAPPY HALLOWEEN MONSTER
BASH!

Page 4
GHOSTS EVERYWHERE!

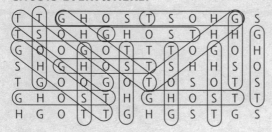

Page 5
FUNNY FACES

HAPPY
SAD
ANGRY
SLEEPY
SURPRISED
SILLY

Page 6–8
TESTING, TESTING!
1. True
2. One
3. Two

4. A spider
5. A witch
6. Witch, pumpkin, black cat
7. THIS WAY TO THE HAUNTED MANSION
8. A skeleton
9. As a cowboy
10. Two bats

Page 9
FRIGHT NIGHT

Pages 10–11
HIDE-AND-SEEK
1. Amy loves playing <u>host</u> at her parents' parties. (ghost)
2. With his quick <u>wit, Ch</u>arles would make a great comedian. (witch)
3. "What's <u>up, Ump?" King</u>sley cheerfully greeted Mr.Townsend, the umpire of his baseball team. (pumpkin)
4. Gra<u>ce met E. R. Y</u>oung at his law office to discuss her case. (cemetery)

5. At Cars & <u>Co., Stu M</u>erriwether is the top salesperson for the fifth year in a row. (costume)
6. Peter and Bo<u>b lack Cat</u>hy's skill at public speaking. (black cat)
7. Pa<u>t, Rick,</u> and Johnny formed a singing group called Punks. (trick)
8. Because I had a li<u>sp, I'd</u>...er...sometimes be self-conscious when I...er...spoke. (spiders)
9. The chef set the slices of ha<u>m on ster</u>ling silver trays. (monster)
10. Cedri<u>c, Andy, Cor</u>nelius, and Simon are on the high school baseball team. (candy corn)

Page 12
HERE A BOO, THERE A BOO!
1. book
2. brook
3. boomerang
4. boom
5. broom
6. balloon
7. bloom
8. blood
9. boots
10. ballroom
11. bridegroom
12. bassoon

Page 13
DOT'S ALL, FOLKS!

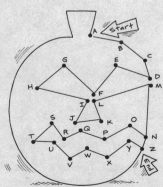

Pages 14–15
WHAT'S THE DIFFERENCE?

Pages 16–17
WORD UP!
Here are some words you will find in GRAVEYARD:
are, dare, dear, drag, dreary, dye, ear, gave, gay, gear,
grade, grave, gravy, gray, rag, rage, rare, rave, ray, read,
ready, rear, red, very, yard, year

Page 18
SEEING DOUBLE

Page 19
ODD ONE OUT

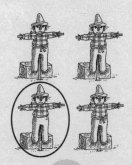

Pages 20–21
MOVIE SCRAMBLE

1. spoon
2. sun
3. gold
4. stay
5. rabbit
6. March

7. large
8. hello
9. Easter
10. buy
11. breakfast
12. chase

GHOSTBUSTERS

Pages 22–23
COSTUME CROSSWORD

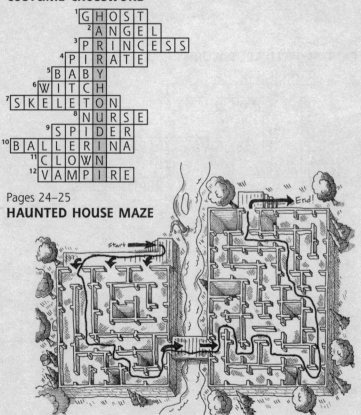

```
        ¹G H O S T
        ²A N G E L
      ³P R I N C E S S
    ⁴P I R A T E
  ⁵B A B Y
⁶W I T C H
⁷S K E L E T O N
      ⁸N U R S E
    ⁹S P I D E R
¹⁰B A L L E R I N A
  ¹¹C L O W N
  ¹²V A M P I R E
```

Pages 24–25
HAUNTED HOUSE MAZE

Start

End!

Pages 26–27
SPIDER HUNT

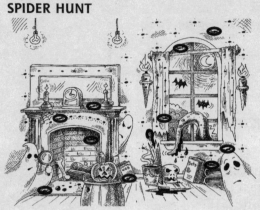

Pages 28–29
CANDY-COATED CROSSWORD

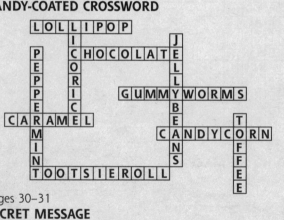

Pages 30–31
SECRET MESSAGE

1. no
2. mow
3. sew
4. ton
5. eye
6. nod
7. yo
8. uu

1	2	3		4	5	6		7	8	9		10	11
N	O	W		Y	O	U		S	E	E		M	E

	12	13	14		15	16	17		18	19	20	21	
	N	O	W		Y	O	U		D	O	N	T	

Page 32
GOING IN CIRCLES
They are world-famous superheroes!

Page 33
THE NAME GAME
1. The Incredible Hulk
2. Batman
3. Wonder Woman
4. Spider-man
5. Superman

Pages 34–35
ORDER! ORDER!

Pages 36–37
HALLOWEEN HA-HA'S
1. He had no guts.
2. She gave him coffin medicine.
3. Do you believe in love at first fright?

Pages 38–39
CREATURE FEATURE
These characters are major movie stars!

```
T  H  E  B  L  O  B  G  N  O  K  G  N  I  K  T  H
H  E  S  T  H  E  W  E  R  E  W  O  L  F  E  C  H
E  A  R  A  C  A  L  U  C  A  R  D  T  N  U  O  C
M  T  E  Y  L  F  E  H  T  H  E  Z  O  M  B  I  E
U  T  H  E  S  W  A  M  P  T  H  I  N  G  R  S  A
M  O  R  N  A  M  F  L  O  W  E  H  T  L  R  E  M  A  J
M  O  R  B  I  G  F  O  O  T  M  L  O  V  I  E  S
Y  T  N  I  E  T  S  N  E  K  N  A  R  F  A  R  S
```

Page 40
MIXED-UP MESS